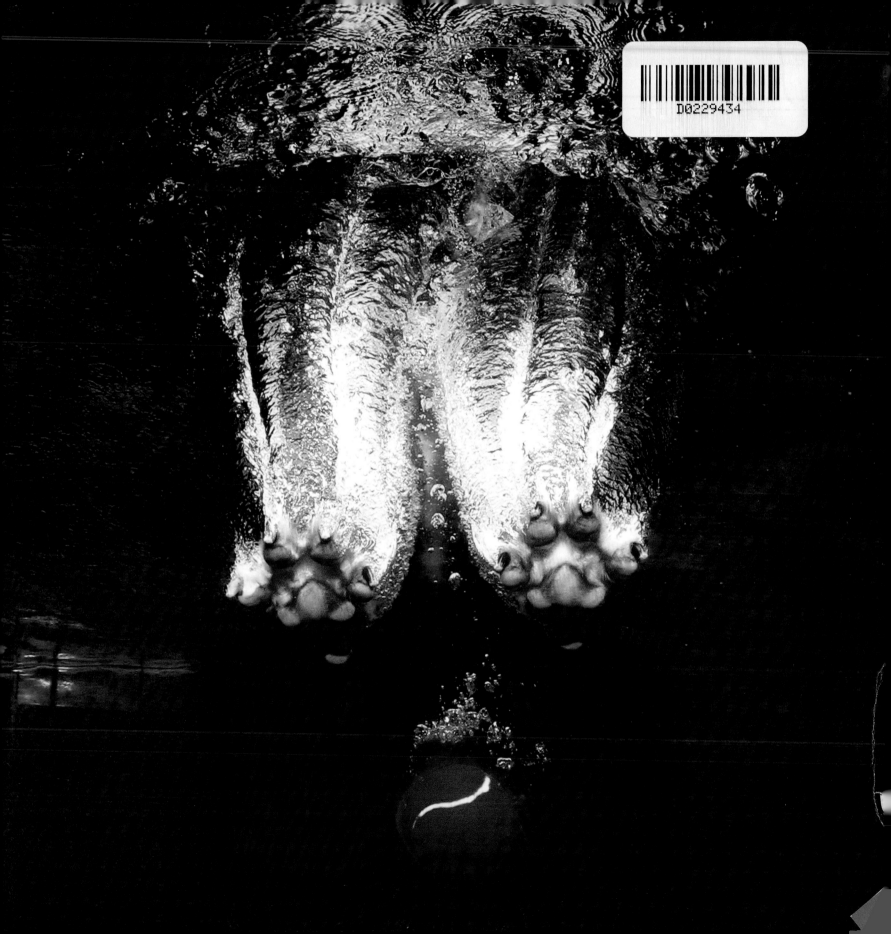

First published in Great Britain in 2013
by HEADLINE PUBLISHING GROUP

1

Cataloguing in Publication Data is available from the British Library

Hardback ISBN 978 1 4722 1148 4

Printed and bound in Great Britain by
Butler Tanner & Dennis Ltd, Frome, Somerset

HEADLINE PUBLISHING GROUP
An Hachette UK Company
338 Euston Road
London NW1 3BH

www.headline.co.uk

Seth Casteel

UNDERWATER
DOGS KIDS EDITION

headline

When I look underwater,
what do I see?

So many doggies

looking at me!

Life's simple things are what dogs enjoy.

There's nothing better than fetching your toy.

Keep your eyes on the prize.
Don't drift astray.

The ball is only a paddle away.

We're just getting started.
The fun doesn't stop.

Who's ready for a big belly FLOP?

Down,

down,

down it goes.

It's right below
your doggy nose.

Give me your paw!
What a glorious dive.
You deserve a **doggy high five!**

Grinning,
happy,
full of joy.

You just found
your favourite toy!

It doesn't matter who gets the toy in the end.

Swimming is best when done with a friend!

Oops – missed it!
Where'd it go?

The ball was here a second ago!

Show me your smile.
You're having fun.

Everyone loves
a day in the sun!

Now try to relax and go with the flow.

Sometimes it's best to take it slow.

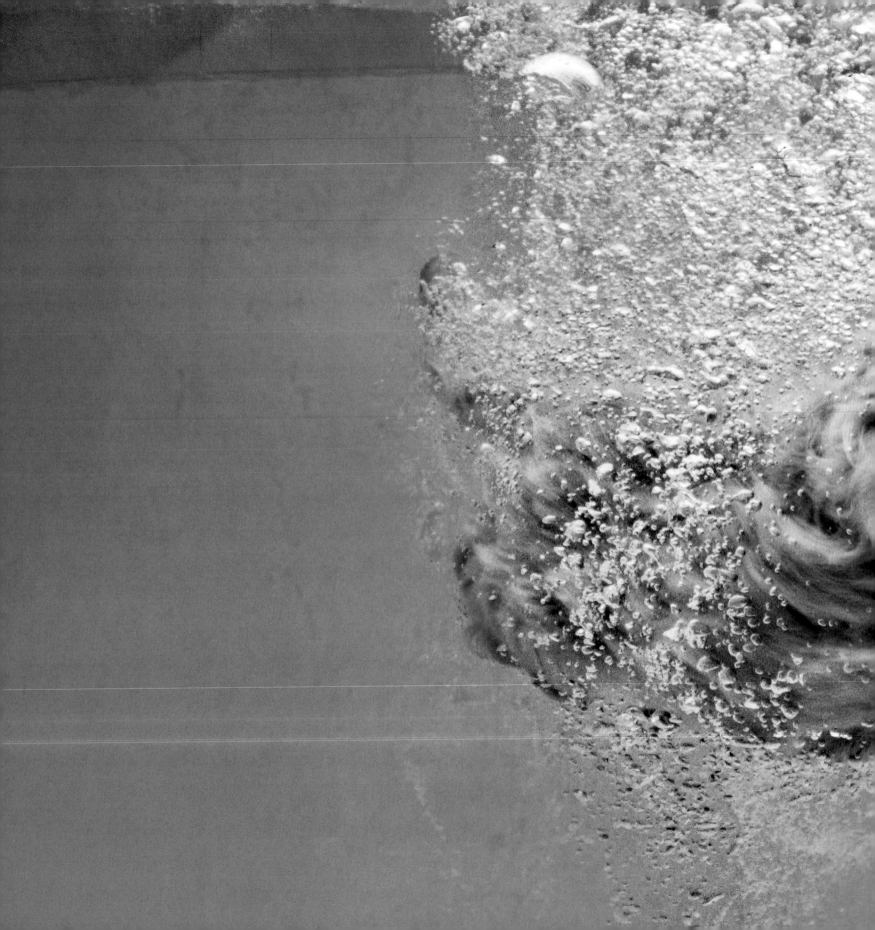

Catching that ring
sure was a breeze.

Look at the camera.
It's time to say
"Cheese!"

A day in the pool
helps you unwind.

Here you can leave all
your worries behind.

THE SWIMMERS...

JAKE, American Pit Bull Terrier

RAIKA, Belgian Tervuren

NEVADA, Border Collie

ROCCO, Boston Terrier

REX, Boxer

WRIGLEY, Boxer–Plott Hound Mix

DAGMAR, Chesapeake Bay Retriever

OSHI, Cocker Spaniel

RHODA, Dachshund

TAG, Dachshund

HERBIE, English Bulldog

CALLAWAY, Golden Retriever

American Pit Bull Terriers: These active and athletic dogs were originally bred to work on farms. One of the most famous pit bulls was a World War I hero named Sergeant Stubby.

Belgian Tervurens: These dogs are very observant! They're especially great as search-and-rescue dogs, helping rescuers find people who are lost.

Border Collies: Smarty-pants! These are perhaps the smartest breed of all. In fact, one border collie named Chaser learned the meaning of over a thousand words!

Boston Terriers: These dogs are known as "American Gentlemen" because of the kind and caring attitudes they have toward their owners. They also are known to snore!

Boxers: Oh boy, oh boy! Boxers are extremely playful! They got their name because they enjoy using their paws to bat at any challengers.

Chesapeake Bay Retrievers: *Quack, quack!* These dogs are great partners for duck hunting. They originated from two puppies that were rescued from a shipwreck in the Chesapeake Bay.

Cocker Spaniels: These dogs are known for their big, floppy, furry ears. You might recognize this breed from the Disney animated film *Lady and the Tramp*.

Dachshunds: These dogs are famous for their short legs and long bodies, which is why they're nicknamed "wiener dogs". Digging is their instinct, so watch out for holes!

English Bulldogs: They might seem grumpy, but don't let their tough exterior fool you. Bulldogs can be very friendly and easygoing. And they enjoy slobbering on everything!

...ON LAND

 CASTER, Golden Retriever

 CLYDE, Golden Retriever

 DUKE, Jack Russell Terrier

 LULU, Jack Russell Terrier

 RUBY, Labradoodle

 APOLLO, Labrador Retriever

 BARDOT, Labrador Retriever

 KING, Labrador Retriever

 WARDEN, Labrador Retriever

 DUNCAN, Pug

 MYLO, Rottweiler

 BRADY, Yorkshire Terrier

Golden Retrievers: Good boy! Golden retrievers love to hang out with people, and they love to play fetch. That instinct comes from being such good helpers to hunters.

Jack Russell Terriers: These little dogs are known to be feisty! They're high-energy, they love attention, and they're great at learning new tricks.

Labradoodles: These hybrids of the Labrador retriever and the poodle were originally bred as guide dogs for people with allergies. So if fur makes you sneeze, these are the dogs for you!

Labrador Retrievers: These dogs are the most popular breed in America and can be yellow, black, or chocolate in colour. Labs' webbed paws make them strong swimmers.

Plott Hounds: What's that smell? These dogs have amazing noses! Their long ears help waft odours up off the ground, which makes Plott hounds great at finding and tracing scents.

Pugs: These little dogs have big personalities! Pugs originated in China and are known for their fondness for kids, as well as their curly tails!

Rottweilers: Sometimes these dogs look tough, but they love to clown around. They are also one of the oldest types of herding dogs, likely dating back to the Roman Empire!

Yorkshire Terriers: These dogs may be small, but they are scrappy, brave, and spunky. They love to cuddle and sit on people's laps. And they have fabulous hair!

A NOTE FROM THE AUTHOR

One day in 2010, I was photographing a dog named Buster in his yard in California. The photo shoot was supposed to be "on land", but Buster decided he would rather jump into the pool. He jumped in over and over again, chasing his favourite tennis ball. I thought, *WOW! I wonder what he looks like underwater.* So I jumped right in! I had so much fun taking pictures of Buster in the water that I decided to swim with and photograph other dogs, too. Since then, I have worked underwater with more than three hundred dogs of all shapes, sizes, colours, and ages. Most of the dogs featured in this book had never been underwater until they met me, and some had never even been swimming. Not only did they participate of their own free will, but they also had a ton of fun!